CREATURES
OF DARKNESS

CREATURES OF DARKNESS

by Esther Baskin

Drawings by Leonard Baskin

An Atlantic Monthly Press Book

Little, Brown and Company, Boston, Toronto

For Toby

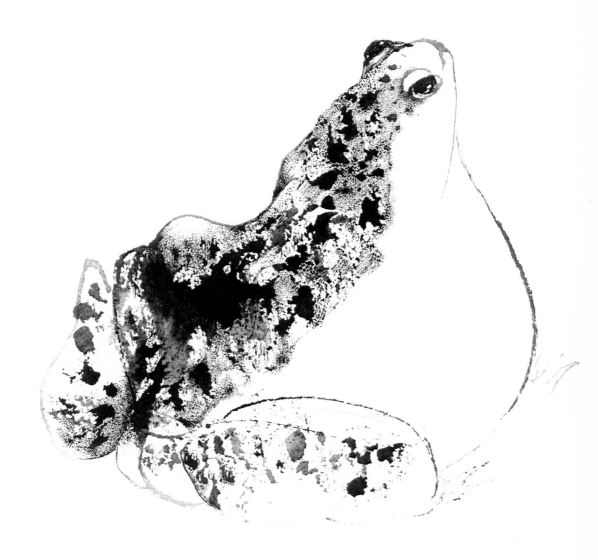

The Frog and the Toad

IT IS a spring evening, and the jack-in-the-pulpit is gay with new green growth. From marsh and pond comes the tuneful chorus of the peepers. They have hibernated all winter, and now the one-inch creatures usher in the spring with their peeping call.

When it rains, toads seem to come from everywhere. Many end up squashed dead on cart-tracks and highways. Toads never drink the rainwater—or any water—but absorb it through their skins. When they hibernate they need no water or food. Cold-blooded creatures, their body temperature is regulated by climatic conditions.

Out from under cool porches and up from damp, dark cellars comes the hoppity nighttime toad. His light-colored throat-sac becomes so distended when he sings full voice that it is larger than his head. Those rare people who know frogs and music say that his sweet song sounds like part of Beethoven's Moonlight Sonata. One says "he" and "his," for only the males sing.

His pimpled, warty back (which does not cause warts) blends well with earthen rocky backgrounds. Depending upon environment, the toad's color can change from yellow to black.

The adult toad changes his skin, or molts, four times a year, the growing tadpole every few weeks. Down to the four fingers of his hand and his five toes with their thick web, his skin is quickly shed. After the skin splits down his back, he tears it away with his mouth. This takes only five minutes, and then he swallows his skin.

His enormous, protruding eyes with their golden irises are brilliant and beautifully gemlike. So comes the notion of a jewel buried in the toad's head which acts as a talisman to ward off evil. From Shakespeare comes this bit of an appropriate poem:

> The ungainly toad
> That crawls from his secure abode,
> Within the mossy garden wall,
> When evening dews begin to fall.
> Oh, mark the beauty of his eye,
> What wonders in that circle lie!
> So clear, so bright, our fathers said—
> "He wears a jewel in his head."

He is the gardener's ally, for he eats harmful insects. Only moving creatures are his fare and these he eats sitting up, statuesque in pose. He has no teeth and swallows insects whole, and occasionally his sides twitch as the live insect struggles in his stomach. As a deadly hunting weapon he has an ingeniously wrought tongue. Because his sticky tongue is attached to the front of his mouth, he is able to dart it out like an arrow and flick it quickly at fast-flying flies. He gulps with difficulty a great June bug, and his eyes retreat into the roof of his mouth as he strains to swallow. Seldom does he eat worms. Because of their slime and prickly spines he finds them awkward and vile, but occasionally he eats one, head first.

When annoyed, toads give off a colorless, odorless fluid that coats their skin with mucus. When frightened, they exude from their skin a more acrid and slightly poisonous liquid unpleasant to their enemies. But rather than trust to their slippery wetness, they may play possum and fall on their backs as if dead. To escape an enemy or when glutted by their ravenous eating, they back into burrows dug with their hardened, spurred legs. They may collapse their burrows around them and bury themselves.

It takes two and sometimes three seasons for the tadpole to become a deadly bullfrog. A tadpole can regenerate his tail should it be bitten off by a fish. As he becomes a frog, the tadpole "eats" his tail by absorbing it into his body.

The nasty bullfrog matures in summer when ponds are grand with arrowhead, pickerel weed and water lily. He enters deep water as well as shallow and prefers to hunt near home. Leaping three feet into a tranquil pond, he swims a powerful stroke very much like our breast stroke, with legs akimbo. He has no outer ear to hinder him. With his nostrils closed, he can live for months at a time under water. He doesn't use his lungs, for his skin acts as a gill.

This nighttime stalker camouflages himself by changing color from light green to near black. The bullfrog is the lone wolf of the pond. All alone he calls, and there is no answering chorus of sound. If he hears any sound, he raises his voice in song, like a bass viol's aria.

The bullfrog is the green dragon of his pond. He eats any small creature, fish or waterlogged animal. A sparrow, wounded or refreshing himself at the shore, can be gobbled up. The heinous bullfrog is also a cannibal. When attacked, he gives forth an almost human, high-pitched, prolonged scream of distress and anguish.

The Weasel

A WEASEL IS many things, all evil. A list of his close relations includes: ferret, wolverine, glutton, stoat, ermine, mink, marten, sable, foumart, polecat, pine-weasel, genet, otter, ratel, civet, badger, skunk, grison, stinking polecat, stifling or squashy skunk, coati, ichneumon and mongoose.

Slyly and stealthily, the weasel slinks along. He can wind like a worm into narrow crevices and small holes and is able to crawl straight up a wall. Long and low-down, he is but two and a half inches high, and seven long. He sniffs along the ground after prey, very much like a dog. The weasel drinks the blood of all he eats, loving to suck the eggs of birds and slaying young rather than old hens. He attacks the head and throat of animals with his fatal bite. The wound the weasel inflicts is so small that to see it one must search for it. For any one creature the weasel kills for food, he kills at least ten for the brutal pleasure of it. He prefers to eat flesh when it has putrefied, and he may happily nest inside a dead animal.

Most of these creatures have a gland beneath their tail which emits a foul, unctuous odor when they are frightened. The

sweet-mart and the civet are exceptions. The emission of the civet is used as a perfume base; even the skin and excrement of the sweet-mart have a sweet smell. The foumart's name means "foul marten." He emits an awful stench. The skunk's putrescent effluvium has a luminescence and can cause blindness. Blindness, too, can come from the urine of the ichneumon. Skunks have been called *enfants du diable* in France.

The weasel-kind have whiskers just like a cat's and a loose skin which makes them difficult to hold. Accosted, they show their teeth, arch their backs and hiss like cats. They all have very sharp claws and, though the smallest of carnivores, are the most bloodthirsty and predacious. They are most powerful, all out of proportion to their size.

The natural life of the weasel and all of its kind is endlessly varied. Martens are oddly afflicted with fits, a kind of epilepsy. They walk on their toes instead of on the entire paw. American martens become scarce every ten years and no one knows why. They eat porcupines, quills and all, which eventually work themselves out through their flesh and skin. Pine martens ravish pine tops and cones. A coati will gnaw its own tail, as if mad. The ratel enjoys eating honey, to

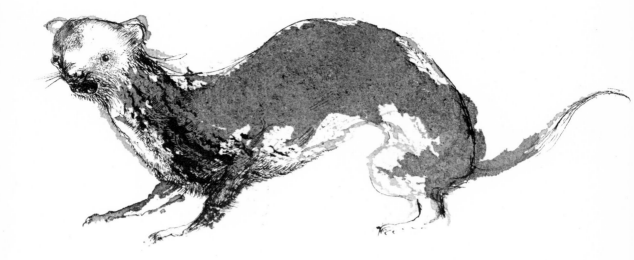

which it is led by birds called honey-guides. Bees cannot sting the ratel because of his shaggy fur. The wolverine, sometimes called glutton, eats the brains and drinks the blood before devouring a helpless creature. (The Mexican skunk relishes only the brains.) Freshly buried flesh is joyously eaten by the gluttonous glutton. A story (we think apocryphal) is told about a glutton's climbing up a tree and throwing moss into the middle of a herd of reindeer. While the reindeer were busy eating the moss, down in their midst leapt the glutton to devour them. At daylight, the wolverine burrows into his nest, rolls himself up into a ball, covers his head with his fat tail and falls asleep.

Brought from Africa to Greece and Spain to take the place of the Egyptian cat, the ferret was tamed and kept as a killer of vermin and rabbits. Now he is kept in barns to kill rats. He often eats his own young, and harms children in their cradles. And his wounds are extremely difficult to cure.

The badger is a bit of a clown. He can walk or trot backwards. He loves the liquor of decayed fruit. He carefully soaks all his food in spring water. Artists, good and indifferent, use brushes made from his fur. The verb "to badger" comes from the pesky nature of badgers.

The ichneumon, like the mongoose, kills and eats deadly snakes. He was worshiped as a god in ancient Egypt because he eats the eggs and young of crocodiles.

The furs of the ermine, otter, marten, mink and sable are very valuable, especially when the animal comes thickly furred from the north. In summer, the ermine is a stoat, not at all white but a dirty yellow, and not valuable. Sable are hunted with traps or blunt weapons so as not to injure the fur. An artist's sable brush, although it is expensive, is a great asset because it comes to a fine point when wet.

According to Aristotle, the sable is an aquatic animal—which is not true. But the mink is aquatic and fish-eating. An otter, too, truly water-loving, eats fish and when he tires of that diet sometimes a very young lamb. Young otters will coast down a snowy hill for fun, using their backsides as sleds.

A weasel takes to the water only if he has to. It has been told that an eagle who flew away with a weasel in his talons had finally to drop him when the fierce little creature painfully bit his throat. Leonardo da Vinci painted one of his typically haunted women holding, catlike, a creature of the weasel family. Even though the painting is called "Woman with Weasel," the animal she holds is actually an ermine. Its whiteness symbolizes the virtue of chastity, and we know a weasel is not white but a dirty yellow-brown.

Game wardens in England have a kind of fence, called a "vermin" pole, upon which they hang the destructive creatures they kill. There one can see dead falcons, foxes, woodchucks, owls and, above all, weasels. Some are freshly hung (like drying clothes), others wasted, decomposed, in all states of putrescence, dry and skeleton-like.

The Nightjar

THE NIGHTJAR, with great gaping mouth, flies through
the dusky forest and heath ahunt for insects and moths.
His mouth is a capacious trap to catch small flitterers in the
twilight air. Like an owl's, his head and eyes are large, as he
flies noiseless through the umbrage. Of crepuscular habits, he
sees but dimly by day. He does not perch on a branch but
horizontally strides it, screeching his harsh and raucous jarring
call.

Brother to the nightjar, or nighthawk, is the lonely whip-
poorwill with his plaintive, haunted cry.

The nightjar is also known as the goatsucker: this because
in Italy and Greece he is thought to suck the milk from goats.
Aristotle has it that this milk-sucking bird causes the goat to
go dry and blind.

The Wolf

THE WOLF, a terror to animal and man alike, walks about in night forests and isolated villages. He is the unlordly would-be lion of the wilderness, cunningly cautious and a coward. He walks slyly on his toes and hunts in packs. He has a keen sense of smell for flesh and carrion. He appears in times of distress and war and disentombs poorly buried bodies. He seeks living meat rather than dressed flesh. Every creature is his prey, but once he has tasted human flesh he then prefers it even to the horseflesh he craves.

Wolves wreak havoc on herds, one distracting the prey while the others bloodily attack. The wolf attacks the throats of animals, seizes the flanks and bites the hocks, mouthing an awesome mass of flesh. He bears away a sheep, whole, in his mouth that may drip hydrophobia. To all other animals his flesh is vile, so that only a wolf willingly eats a wolf. When their bellies are empty of flesh, hating emptiness, they fill them with swamp mud and then disgorge it when they find food.

Called the dog of the woods, he can, as a related species, interbreed with dogs. A sleeping man in a tent may have his provisions stolen from under his very head by the wolf. Wolves make a regular trodden track, as if they walked single file like Indians, to their dens in the woods.

There are wolves in all climates, cold and hot. In India's heat, to save their foot-pads from scorching, they hide from the midday sun. It took the power and regal fortitude of many kings of England to abolish wolves in that land, and they were finally extirpated in the early eighteenth century. In England during the tenth-century reign of King Edgar, the tax on silver and gold could be paid with wolves' tongues. A goodly number of these tongues could buy pardon for an outlaw. Land, too, was held on the condition of slaying a quota of fierce wolves. Annually, there was a day given to a "wolfe-hunt," and January was called the "wolfe-month" because of the wolves' prevalence. A person outside the pale of the law, an outlaw, was killed "like a wolf" and was then called a "wolfes-head."

In the time of the great bison herds, roaming wolves, fat and almost tame—if wolves can be said to be "almost tame"—

would haunt our lonely Western villages. Indians used the wolf cautiously as a kind of dog for hunting the bison. The fur of the wolf they wore for warmth and the wolf's skin made excellent parchment for their resounding drumheads. When wolves attacked the bison, they killed only the ill and young among them, fearful of their glorious strength.

Once a man carrying a fiddle was cornered by a wolf. He quickly climbed a tree and, in his fright, broke a fiddle string. The wolf was terrified and stilled at the whining sound. This

time the maw of the wolf lost its feast. It is reported that experiments at the Zoological Gardens in London showed it to be true that a wolf would stop aghast in his tracks all atremble at the sound of a stringed instrument.

Superstitions and legends tell of wolves rearing children. The twins Romulus and Remus, mythical founders of Rome, were raised by a notorious she-wolf. But it is more likely that a wolf, finding babes, would carry them off and devour them.

The old Anglo-Saxon myth of werewolves tells of men diabolically bewitched into the temporary or permanent shape of a wolf with a tremendous yearning for flesh and blood.

We all know the story of Little Red Riding Hood, but here is a Russian tale about a woman in a sledge and a wolf. It is known that Russians have been notoriously afflicted by wolves. Once, a wolf accosted a woman and three children in a sledge, with furious open mouth and daring leaps. Over snowy fields and past icy bushes and trees dashed the sledge and its terrified riders, with the wolf gnashing hot behind. When they drew near to the village and the wolf was almost at their throats, to save the others the woman threw one of her children to the wolf. As the race grew more frightful, she wantonly cast the second and then the last of her children to the deadly hunter. While the glutted marauder was eating the last child, she stumbled almost lifeless into the village. A peasant, when he heard the tale, was so outraged at this woman who had saved her own life by sacrificing her children that he cleft her skull in two with an axe.

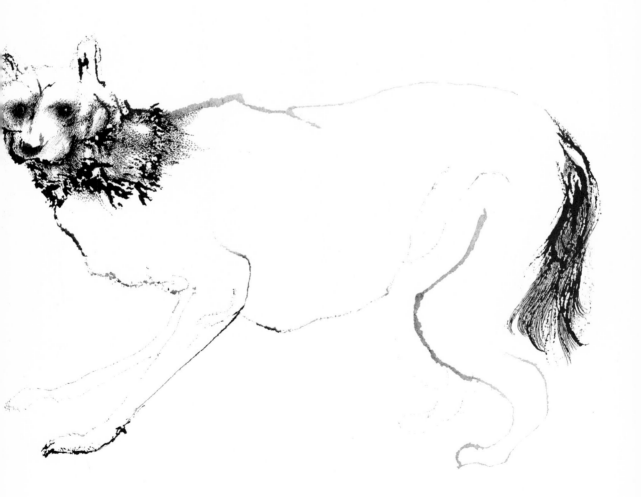

The Firefly

THE FIREFLIES spangle the dark like flashing sequins and flaming meteors. In the West Indies and South America, they are so large and bright they can be attached to the wrist or ankle as a light for fishing or hunting; or placed in a jar to serve as a light for reading or illumination for an evening's garden partly. For such a party, women in Havana buy fireflies as headdress ornaments. Like the moth, fireflies are attracted by light and will land all aglimmer on firebrands. Since the dead bodies of lightning bugs remain luminous for a while, rubbing them on the face makes it glow weirdly ghost-like, to frighten women and children.

To us, the firefly exists to spatter the evening with shimmer. But, alas, it is no innocent, for it feeds upon the harmless forest snail. The firefly sinks its fierce jaw into the snail's thin skin and paralyzes its victim. Erosive liquids are poured into the numbed snail which slowly corrode its tissues. All of the snail's body fluids are finally sucked up by the firefly through its tubular jaw very much in the way a thick malted is sipped through a straw.

The wingless glowworm is the female firefly. Her flickering light is a mating signal, and the varied rhythm of its flashing tells a zoologist which species she is. Even the firefly's eggs warmly shine at night.

When the lightning bug is placed in cold water its phosphorescence disappears, but warm water makes it brilliant. Unlike an electric bulb, which gives heat, the firefly's gleam is completely cold. This cold light comes from the presence of luciferin (after Lucifer, the angel of hellish fire), a substance in the firefly's body which when exposed to air produces the scintillating light.

In the nineteenth century, the sparkling of the firefly was thought to lead the nightingale to food. Superstitious people also supposed its mystic brightness was a "holy light" that told of a departed soul's resting place. Sadly, the Irish cannot think this, for there are no lightning bugs in Ireland.

Like many poets who wrote verse about the "glimmering glowworm," Gilbert White, the eighteenth-century naturalist, wrote this little poem in a letter to a friend:

> The chilling night-dews fall: away, retire;
> For see, the glow-worm lights her amorous fire!
> Thus, ere night's veil had half obscured the sky,
> Th' impatient damsel hung her lamp on high;
> True to the signal, by love's meteor led,
> Leander hastened to his Hero's bed.

The Rat

THE BLACK RAT is thinner and somewhat smaller than his fat and rapacious cousin, the brown or Norway rat— (7 inches long as against 11 inches, excluding the tail which measures about 8 inches in both). He is fairly timid, for a rat, and hesitates to fight back when attacked. It is only his muscular body that aids his lithely leaping scurrying dash of an escape. Nevertheless, he is not fast enough and is almost extinct, overcome by the voracious and larded-o'er brown rat.

As a Malthusian* nicety, the population of the prolific rat is controlled by his cannibalistic propensity. Since rats bear three litters of twelve and more offspring a year, in no time at all they would outnumber their human neighbors. The feeble and sickly ones amongst them are devoured and room is left for the viciously strong and the agressive young ones. With great finesse and uncanny skill, they turn the skins of their victims inside out down to the very toes, leaving not a shred of flesh behind. Rather than say "dog eats dog," to say "rat eats rat" goes more to the heart of the matter. Rats, when cornered and famished, have been known to attack humans.

Like a monkey's, the rat's tail is prehensile. The rat uses it as a hand to grasp narrow ledge and rail. It enables him to scale high walls, equipping him well in his maraudings. The rat uses his tail in plunder and carnage to swing agilely up and down steep, slippery surfaces. Rudderlike it steers and balances his fat, swollen body. This snakelike, restless and quivering tail is composed of a chain of little bones laced with muscles, armored with scales and sheathed with long and bristly hairs. There is a story told of a rat who, repeatedly dipping his great tail into a long-necked bottle of oil, was able to lick away its contents.

In a section of Paris known as Montfaucon, there used to be an old slaughterhouse for decrepit horses. From their flesh was produced prussiate of potash, a chemical used in the making of the artist's most esteemed color of Prussian blue, while the

* Footnote for curious readers: The Englishman Thomas Robert Malthus was a nineteenth-century political economist and preacher. His pessimistic theory of population growth held that natural disasters, war, disease and abstention from marriage were necessary to help equalize the world's speedily growing population with the food supply.

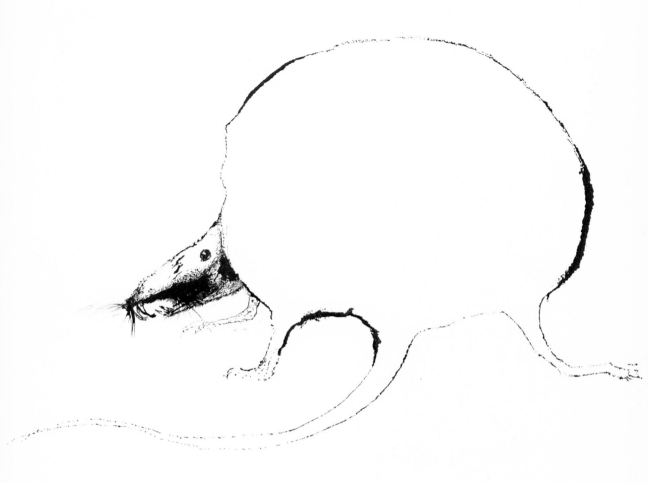

bones were ground into fertilizer. The abattoir abounded in fat and fearless rats who cleaned up whatever flesh fell to the slimy stone floor. Once, when the rats got too overwhelmingly numerous, the workers caught and killed some 15,000 in a month's time! There was a rumor that their skins were made into fancy gloves to be sold in elegant Parisian shops—but no Parisian glove-seller ever admitted to knowledge of this tale. (A Cornishman once made himself a complete garb from head to toe, hat and shoes included, out of rat skins—670 to be exact, which took him three years to amass.)

At one time it was planned to move the Montfaucon abattoir to the outskirts of town. But since the rat population in the slaughterhouse was thought to outnumber the human population—even unto all the people of Paris—it was feared that the people would be left the sole prey of the ravaging rats.

The Moth

MOTHS FLY LISTLESSLY through the night mists. Some, like the dancing stellata, are as small as flies and others, like the Luna moth, are as grotesquely large as birds. Adult moths never eat, for they have no stomachs. Generally their vivid color makes them look much like camouflaged cloth. Quivering and agasp in search of light and fire, they end their short lives in it and burn in an auto-da-fé.

The Hedgehog

THE HEDGEHOG'S nightly feedings consist of insects, bird's eggs, fruits, rats and other small animals. Armored with harsh spines and prickles, the hedgehog when frightened rolls himself into a fat ball. When he is irritated, he wheezes asthmatically, grunts and points his spines forward. Unafraid, he sharply nips a young weasel or a mouse. He kills snakes, impervious to their bite, and devours them tail-first. The cantharides or Spanish fly is eaten by hedgehogs, though it is harmful and anathema to all other animals. Rolled into a prickly ball, he can drop from a great height without injuring himself. Into forest hole and hedgerow hedgehogs go to rest from their nighttime labors.

In the winter, the hedgehog hibernates, covering himself with leaves and dried grass and looking very much like a clump of mulch left to rot. He is capable of being domesticated, and like a dog, he answers to his name. He eats cockroaches in the kitchens of England.

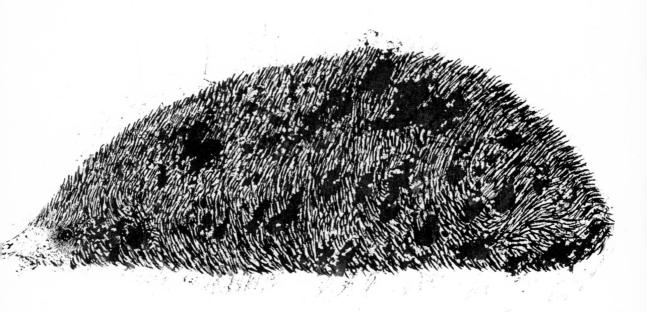

The Bat

THE BAT, with his ghastly and ghostly face, evil and dark, is a being all hideous and vile who terrifies with staring, haunting eyes. He is a creature of our nightmares and blackened hallucinations, an apparition never really seen, who flits and hovers in our blinded thoughts. Bats, dim and formless, dreaming through the riven earth, wandering lost in moonlit fields, are visitors and sleepers in darkened sepulchres and dismal catacombs.

There is a fine fable about bats. Once, a bat, being overwhelmed by a weasel, pleaded with him and told him that in actuality he was a bird. The weasel, his heart touched (which is very unlike him), let the bat fly away. A little later, the weasel caught the same bat. This time the bat begged him to let him go because, indeed, he was only a meek and measly mouse. Again, the weasel, forgetting what had happened before, released his prey. Thus, we have both aspects of the bat presented to us, his mythic, shrouded being as both rodent and bird.

In past and present art and literature, frightful devils are shown sporting bats' wings. Harpies, those awful omens of the bad and harsh, half human and half bird, were thought to be bats. Their supposed sinful stench alone would explain this notion, since bats have a vomitous and putrescent odor.

The Greek and Hebrew names for a bat mean "flying dark-ness." Among the Chinese, the bat is a symbol of good luck. In the West, we believe anything but that. A bat's wing is a choice ingredient of many a witch's brew and is used in unholy herbal remedies.

During the Civil War there were guards stationed in bat caves to protect the bat dung or guano from pilferers. The bat guano was used in the making of niter for gunpowder. Although bat guano is no longer a chief ingredient of gunpowder, it is still expensive as a fertilizer, selling for approximately fifty dollars a ton.

Into the Carlsbad Caverns in New Mexico about nine million bats enter each dawn within twenty minutes. They swoop into the caves, dart and check themselves, capricious and eccentric; rising and falling as if wafted by a wind, they flutter about laboriously through the dark air, very unlike birds, rather more like large Luna moths. If their flight resembles that of any bird, it is the questioning flight of the swift.

While in the caves, the bats are disorderly, yapping and chattering, pushing and nipping each other, vying for position, the larger ones preying upon the smaller with their formidable teeth. The big-eared bat, fluttering his long, sensitive ears as a mark of anger, frightens off all other bats in the vicinity.

In the cave the ground glistens with silver, silver from the insect wings the bat discards after he has eaten the fleshy parts. A bat can eat the equivalent of his weight daily in insects.

While a bat sleeps, he fans himself with his spidery, weblike wings, the wings ending in hands—rather claws or hooks—helping him to seize his prey. A bat never walks on two or four feet but crawls using the thumb- and toenails of all four claws. A bat sleeps hanging upside down—we don't know why.

The eyes of a bat are very small, shiny and beady. They are deeply imbedded, generally black, and very much like a mole's. Spallanzani, in the eighteenth century, suspended many wires in a room in which he kept blinded bats. These bats were able to avoid collision with the wires about eighty per cent of the time. Today we know it was because of that mysterious phenomenon called sonar. With their delicately attuned hearing, bats can pick up their own reverberating calls bouncing off any object.

A bat, when he hibernates in winter, sleeps hanging upside down, looking very much like a closed black umbrella. His temperature drops to 50 degrees Fahrenheit from a norm of 104 degrees and he breathes only four to six times an hour. His body processes, including his heartbeat, slow down almost to a halt.

Just before bats begin to hibernate they mate, the seed remaining inside the female until spring when it fertilizes the female egg. Female bats have a scent gland, a swelling on the upper lip which emits a musky odor attractive to the male bat.

The young bats—the brood is usually one or two—have no nest or shelter. The mother carries them about clinging to her breast and suckling there.

Enemies of the bat are few. Sometimes a chicken or pilot black snake pursues one into his roost or tree hollow and swallows him whole. In the early morning when bats enter the Carlsbad Caverns, there are about 60 to 100 falcons, kites and crows out for the sport of bat-catching. Often, these birds enter the cave to do their killing. The falcon, like the snake, sometimes swallows the bat whole. Oppossums and skunks, too, have been known to eat bats.

Often a bat drops into water to elude a pursuer, and then swims ashore using his wings as paddles. At night, bats skim along the waters of a pond or river to drink. They also catch fish, or, when no fish are obtainable, they gaily munch, crunching a green frog. Indeed, there are bats called fishing bats.

In a large spider web the smaller bats, like the gay little Pipistrelle, are sometimes enmeshed. The bat eats the spider; but at times, if it is a large spider, the spider eats the bat. Occasionally bats are caught tangled in electric wires, thereby electrocuting themselves. It must be said, however, that these are not very common ways of dying for bats.

Bats are host to fleas, tapeworms, bedbugs and lice. They can, at times, pass on these vermin to human beings. Although a bat cleans himself very much like a cat, scratching and licking, he still can't rid himself of his vermin.

Rabies has of late afflicted bats. When a bat is rabid, he flies about in the daylight, fights, mauls and consumes other bats, bitterly and irritably biting anything he can find, including human beings. In our Southern states, a few children have been bitten by such bats. Some have died from the bites. Unfortunately, the Carlsbad Caverns are now infested with these rabid bats and we have to beware.

Vampire bats live only in the tropics of South America and Africa. They most often sully sleeping fowl, mules, cows, sheep

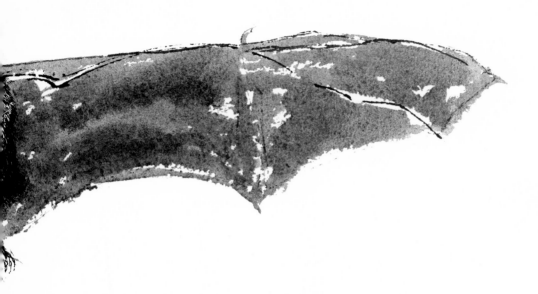

and horses, but occasionally will kill and eat other bats that offend them. Farmers frequently put up wire nets to protect their livestock. Indeed, many animals are so sapped of strength and blood that they die.

A vampire finds a man sleeping with his hands, feet or face exposed. Delicately the vampire cuts away the hair and skin, clearing a spot to be sucked. This it does, supposedly, without causing pain. With its blade-like front teeth it incises a sharp, clean cut and lets just enough blood ooze out for it to lap up, taking about twenty minutes to drink its fill. The tongue of the vampire is encrusted with horny papillae or nipples, the better to suck blood with. The blood is held for a time in its mouth, to be swallowed at leisure, while it fans its sleeping prey to keep it from awakening. Blood is the only food it eats.

963/5

There are bats that act like flowers, leaf-nosed bats, for instance. In their search for insects and nectar they cover themselves with pollen and, going from flower to flower, cross-fertilize them. Once in a while, digging for insects, they tear flowers to shreds or strew petals about, often leaving tooth and claw marks as signs of their visitation.

In the Equatorial regions, tiny bats hollow out bamboo stalks for beds or cut palm fronds in such a way as to make a kind of bower in which to fold themselves in sleep.

Egypt's great Pyramids are haunted by bats, darkly called tomb bats, death's very witnesses, who wander hopelessly about the mummies.

Bats can live many years. Indeed, there was a bat in a zoo who lived for 25 years.

Flying foxes or fruit bats in Java and the Equatorial regions have a wing span of more than five feet. They are wanton despoilers of fruit and cause the planter frightful losses. Fruit bats at times drink so much of the palm tree juice that they stagger about as if drunk. When they hang from the trees, sleeping by day, they look like ripe papayas.

These huge bats are considered by some to be great and delicious delicacies of cuisine. So, the expropriators are expropriated. Of grotesque size and foxlike face, they look very much as if they were imprisoned in the guise of bats, pleading and straining to be released—free to roam the dark abysses, batlike again.

In appearance, all the harmless and innocent bats look the most atrocious and hideous, while the vampires, those denizens of unholy places—frightening bloodletters—have almost human, dreaming faces.

One supposes that because of the bewilderment, curiosity and terror bats have inspired, people sought a way to handle their thoughts and fears, finding metaphoric names to express their feelings, tremors and terrors.

All in all, there are approximately 2000 species of bat. We list some of their names:

1. Bamboo bat
2. Black-and-white bat
3. Bloodsucking vampire bat
4. Bogey bat
5. Butterfly bat
6. Cave bat
7. Centurion bat
8. Cicada bat
9. Cluster bat
10. Collared bat
11. Cusped-tooth bat
12. Disc-winged bat
13. Dusky bat

14. Epaulet bat
15. Fish-eating bat
16. Flower-nosed bat
17. Flying fox
18. Fringed bat
19. Frosted bat
20. Fruit bat
21. Funnel-eared bat
22. Ghost bat
23. Golden bat
24. Gray-headed bat
25. Guano bat
26. Hairy-armed bat
27. Hammer-headed bat
28. Harelipped bat
29. Harlequin bat

30. Heraldry bat
31. High-browed bat
32. Hoary bat
33. Hollow-faced bat
34. Horseshoe bat
35. House bat
36. Javelin bat

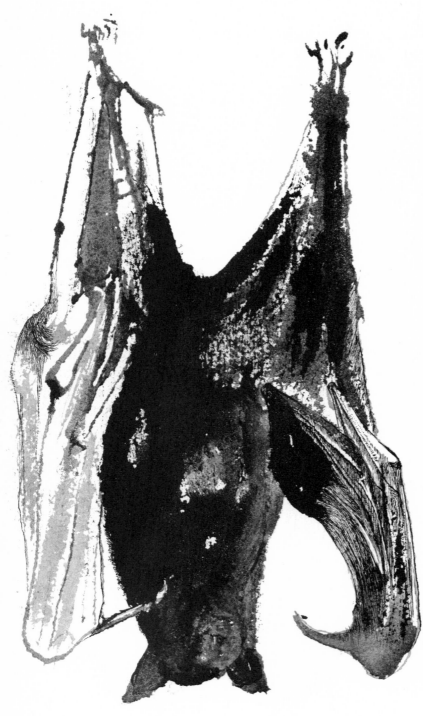

37. Little bulldog bat
38. Little pallid bat
39. Lobe-lipped bat
40. Long-fingered bat
41. Long-legged bat
42. Lump-nosed bat
43. Mastiff bat
44. Mountain bat
45. Mouse-tailed bat
46. Naked bat
47. Noctule bat
48. Pale cave bat
49. Particolored bat
50. Pigmy canyon bat
51. Pig-nosed bat
52. Pipistrelle
53. Pouch-winged bat
54. Sac-winged bat
55. Sheath-tailed bat
56. Shrewlike vampire bat
57. Silver haired bat
58. Snub-nosed bat
59. Spear-nosed bat
60. Spectacled bat
61. Smoky bat
62. Specter bat
63. Straw-colored bat
64. Sucker-footed bat
65. Tomb bat
66. Tricolor bat
67. Twilight bat
68. Vampire bat
69. Vespertilio
70. Whiskered bat
71. White-bellied bat
72. Wrinkled-lipped bat

The May Beetle and the Pyrgota Fly

THRASHING AGAINST the window of a lighted room
on a late spring night, frantically attacking and crashing
headlong till it seems the force of their armored bodies must
shatter the glass, are the May beetles.

Flying amidst these bumbling heavy creatures is the delicately elongated wasplike pyrgota fly, the beetle's swift and
deadly enemy. The beetle flies, dashing at the light, its wings
spread wide, and precisely when the wings are opened at their
widest, the darting pyrgota dives onto the beetle's exposed
back. Then she quickly sinks her daggerlike ovipositor into
the softest and fattest part of the beetle's body, leaving an egg
behind.

As dawn comes, the stricken beetle, shying from the daylight, burrows into the soil as is its wont. But the beetle's days are marked. The larva of the fly buried in the beetle's body begins to feed on its fluid and tissues; and as the beetle grows weaker and weaker, the pyrgota larva grows larger and stronger. After several days, the May beetle can barely stir itself for the evening's mad dance against the lighted window and then can only rest in its burrow. The pyrgota larva within the beetle's body so devours muscle and nerve that the beetle dies. Thus the fat larva becomes a scavenger and hollows out the dead beetle's body, leaving nothing but the once clamoring shell. The pyrgota larva now lies within the empty shell, quietly awaiting the next spring when it will emerge as an adult pyrgota fly.

The Owl

INDEED, THE OWL is a much maligned bird. It is an insect-catcher and a busy and efficient destroyer of grain-eating rodents, the rapacious executioner of wheat-fattened rats, moles, mice and voles. Certainly, the owl is a heavyweight in the balance of nature.

Nonetheless, there is something about owls that has caused dread and foreboding. They have inspired myths of diabolic intent and dark superstitions of ill omen. It is an owl's wing that is the crowningly potent ingredient the Witches add to their noisome brew in *Macbeth*. Spenser calls the owl "the ill-faced oule, Death's dreaded messenger." In Spain, the tawny owl (said by Thomas Bewick, a nineteenth-century engraver and naturalist, to fastidiously pluck the feathers of birds he kills before eating them) is thought of as the Devil's own bird, a drinker of sacramental oil from out the lamps of saints' shrines. Shakespeare voiced these gloomy sentiments with his "Out ye owls, nothing but songs of death!"

What is it about the owl that preys so on our fearful imagination? What makes the owl hover so about our dark and drear frights, an unknown and quivering fear rising not clearly seen, only glimpsed as a dim flitting specter caught out of the corner of our eye, as a winging movement, careening in the twilight of

shadow, wheeling, gliding and circling through black forests? He utters strange screeches, moaning shrieks, hysterical sobs, or mournful questionings as he floats softly ahush. His feathers are soft and cushioned, muffling the fluttering of his wings. They silence any warning and render his flight noiseless, mysteriously sourceless and unnatural. As he floats adrift in moonlight, this shy creature courts lonely woods, deserted buildings and graveyards, preferring the retirement and security of darkness. Wandering alone in night forest and field, he is uninterested in congregating in friendly fashion with others of his kind.

He dwells in a daylight of darkness. Unlike other birds, his eyes are frontally located in the disc of his large, flat and intense face, giving it expression akin to humans. Widening and narrowing the whites of his eyes, the owl seems to have a paralyzed and paralyzing stare as he transfixes his prey, impaling with a daggerlike look.

Silent on his branch, the owl tensely observes all movements about him and with his acute hearing strains to catch the rustling of a mouse, yards away in the grass.

In order to watch a moving creature the owl has to turn his head, since his eyes are fixed in their sockets. It is humorously told that an owl will twist his head off watching a man go round and round beneath his perch.

Sometimes an owl looks like a little fat wrestler with a belligerently conceited stance: all head, puffy body and no neck. Or like a jack-in-the-box he perpetually stretches up and then retracts his head and body.

Daylight is the owl's darkness and sunrise his twilight. He is almost blind in the light and sleeps, eyes open, on high branches in the forest. Should he be disturbed in his brooding sleep, he moodily disengages himself from the camouflaging branch, but only to stumble clumsily about, dazed and hypnotized by the alien and sickening light. No longer the swift terror of the night, if forced to wing, defenseless, he is beset by a gathering swarm of little daytime birds. Made brave now by his weakened state, they hound and torment him, ridiculing his predicament.

His foreign names, singing out in somber colors and harshly strident tones, echo the awe and dread of the owl. The French in a gust of wind breathe "Hibou" while the Italians cough out their "Gufo." "Buho" is softly trod by the Spaniards, as the Germans roll out their rotund and gloomy "Eule." An American Indian tribe imitates the owl's night shriek by naming him the "Cobadecootsh." Perhaps as startling as the owl's own wheezing and shrill shout is the Celtic name of "Corrasgreachag." The Japanese with a doglike yelp bark out their "Howo-waiwo," and the Arabs spit out their guttural grunt of "Khufj." So do these owlish names, raucously and disharmoniously expectorated, mirror our distaste and terror of the owl.

The Bedbug

THE BEDBUG is a creature of darkness and one the poor know well. From walls and wallpaper, mattress creases and bed springs, come the crawling flat, red bedbugs into the peopled night. They creep and scurry away from any light and wait to do their bloodfeasting in quiet and dark. Squash a bedbug, and its stench assails you darkly and acridly. On the sleeper's body, itching, smarting welts are found in the morning, but no bedbugs; they have gone off to their crevices to hide from the glaring sunlight.

The Burying Beetle

THE BLACK BURYING BEETLES, avid undertakers and grave-diggers, scurry into the night to bury the dead, to corrupt the corpses of birds, mice, moles and other small animals. They dig the earth out from under the carcass bit by burdensome bit with their shoveling, spadelike feet. Should a body fall on hard, rocky ground, they slowly drag it to a softer spot to do their nefarious work of inhuming the wreckage of the dead. A bothersome root or limb is bitten away if it encumbers their sepulchral labor. The dead creature is rolled and trussed and becomes a vile, snot-green mass with fur or feathers removed by the ghastly necrophiles. A burial mound is raised around and over this carrion after it sinks into its earthen crypt. This macabre entombment takes only a few hours to achieve. The garbaging of the soil with this graveyard offal serves to manure and mulch it. Surely other appropriate names for the burying beetle are the sexton and the undertaker beetle.

In this morose cemetery the beetles lay their eggs upon the cadaver. The mummylike larvae are fed foul regurgitated flesh by the female beetle, who eats only small morsels of the carcass herself. Because of this ghoulish food, these beetles stink horribly.

The dead bodies have been buried and the beetle's eggs have been laid. Their work in the catacomb is done. As vermin-encrusted elders they mangle and maim one another, battling in a pointless war, and finally eat one another. Rather than digging a grave for one another, to avoid a dotage they easily resort to cannibalism.

The Alley-Cat

AT NIGHT, THE CAT stealthily slinks into backyard and alley. His eyes afire glisten ghastly green. He comes to mate and fight. No more the Egyptian god, he is now a fierce and angry battler being ripped and battered, mauled and scratched. On padded, noiseless feet, he leaps over post and onto fence and serenades his mate with howling and caterwauling. The alley-cat jumps onto a dusty ashcan, uncovers it and rummages in its remnants for filthy food. With his rough, prickly tongue, he licks a meat bone or fish skeleton stark clean. His sense of sight and hearing is so savagely keen that he can elude any unwelcome intruder. The hair on the back of the excitable cat can stand up as if charged with electricity.

In the late nineteenth century, Lord Eldin, an English barrister, kept a loft full of tomcats, for he was amused by them. One night, the cats were overly noisy and raucous. The lord tried to quiet them by ordinary means, but these failing, he seriously and loudly read them the Riot Act. Since they stupidly, he angrily thought, paid it no sensible attention, he had his startled servant horsewhip them.

Ted Hughes, a contemporary English poet, writes this poem about a tomcat:

Esther's Tomcat

Daylong this tomcat lies stretched flat
As an old rough mat, no mouth and no eyes.
Continual wars and wives are what
Have tattered his ears and battered his head.

Like a bundle of old rope and iron
Sleeps till blue dusk. Then reappear
His eyes, green as ringstones: he yawns wide red,
Fangs fine as a lady's needle and bright.

A tomcat sprang at a mounted knight,
Locked round his neck like a trap of hooks
While the knight rode fighting its clawing and bite.
After hundreds of years the stain's there

On the stone where he fell, dead of the tom:
That was at Barnborough. The tomcat still
Grallochs* odd dogs on the quiet,
Will take the head clean off your simple pullet,

Is unkillable. From the dog's fury,
From gunshot fired point-blank he brings
His skin whole, and whole
From owlish moons of bekittenings

Among ashcans. He leaps and lightly
Walks upon sleep, his mind on the moon.
Nightly over the round world of men,
Over the roofs go his eyes and outcry.

* grallochs—disembowels.

The Cockroach

THE COMMON HOUSE ROACH is a scuttling, scurrying dirty yellow creature that feeds on floor crumbs in dark kitchens and carouses in damp bathrooms. The nicest thing about it is its antennae, which have about 80 joints.

DATE DUE

FE 19 63			
DEC 1 1 '68			
MAY 8 1971			
GAYLORD			PRINTED IN U.S.A.